Collector's
Price Guide to PULL TOYS

© 1996

L-W Book Sales
PO Box 69
Gas City, IN 46933

Pictured on introduction pages are
Jacob and Jarrett Wood

ISBN#: 0-89538-049-8

Published by: L-W Book Sales
                  P.O. Box 69
                  Gas City, IN 46933

Printed by IMAGE GRAPHICS, INC., Paducah, Kentucky

Please write for our free catalog.

Table of Contents

Acknowledgments

    We would like to thank the following people for their donation of pull toys to our book:

        Judy Sneed – Hollywood, SC (803)763-7549

        Lynn & Sherilyn Allmond – Brownsboro, TX (903)852-6393

        Doug Moore – Cicero, IN (317)877-1741

Introduction

While the classic pull toy has been around for centuries, imitating simple wheeled technology common to all early civilizations, the focus on collecting pull toys includes items of the post-Victorian era, up to the 1970's. The search for toys predating this period is a very demanding task for a limited few with the resources to do so. The twentieth century provided many mass-produced pull toys to fulfill the wishes of eager imaginative children, and later to appease many toy collectors as well. The pull toy production of toy firms today have been dominated and pushed aside in favor of battery and friction operated playthings.

The immeasurable popularity of the pull toy may have began centuries ago, yet the designs began to emerge into an art form during the late 17th Century. In 1808, William Barton of New York City relocated to East Hampton, CT. Shortly thereafter, his leisure time was consumed in the construction of "bell toys"- simple wood and metal pull toys with figures affixed or somehow connected to a small brass bell. These "bell toys" were vigorously received by children who delighted at the ringing wheeled contraptions. Word spread, and decades later, in 1866, the East Hampton Bell Co. became the Gong Bell Co. in association with Barton. In the same city of East Hampton, a competing company arose in 1884. N. N. Hill Co. was established, and produced a similar line of bell-pull toys. At this point, pull toys of all sorts were soaring in popularity with young ones, and many manufacturers joined the fold. Frantz Mfg. Co., Wyandotte Toys, Fisher Price, and Holgate were a few of the major contributors to the pull toy convoy. Wood was beginning to become the material of choice to manufacturers due to wartime shortages of metal.

Cherished by toy enthusiasts today, pull toys were originally manufactured and marketed with the preschool toddler in mind. These toys need only have a string to grasp and they will anxiously join the adventure of any bounding tot throughout the household where he roams. Many items were more than just a wheeled companion for a toddler's first steps. These items had additional surprises in store to light up a wee child's eyes. They had figures that would move, bounce, spin, ring, ding, clack, or twirl while being drawn across the kitchen floor. Simple mechanisms allowed these toy box wonders to perform any variety of tricks. Colorful paint schemes, vivid labels, and bright lithographs all contributed to the eye-catching graphics of the realm of pull toys.

The interest in all old toys has swelled enormously in the past decade and a half. Particularly noticeable among toy collectors and dealers today are the armies of marching pull toys. The varieties of all these toys about are multiplied when one considers the condition they prefer of items in their collection. As pull toys were notoriously sent sprawling down stairs of steps, launched airborne from kitchen counters, and perilously left within reach of pets large and small, the condition in which they appear in today's collectible market is often questionable by some. Aged specimens in this category are often chipped, scratched, sun bleached, bent, broken, or in sad stages of repair. Therefore, many dabblers in the antique toy market may allow damaged pieces in their collection, while some collectors will only accept the most pristine items. This creates many contradictory opinions when scouting throughout the current collectible toy scene, because these items in mint condition are practically as rare as a prototype for the item. Personal discretion (as well as value) varies immensely from dealer to dealer, as you are familiar with or shall

soon discover. Once you attain a good idea of what all is available out there, then your collection will proceed sharply in whichever direction you prefer.

The collectible toy market has grown on such a massive scale that finding enviable pieces will be easy until a budget is concerned. Collector's malls, shops, and antique dealer shows will provide a trove of toys to behold, yet collectors' publications provide even more of a wide range of both items and prices. The key here is while balancing appropriations with other collectors, always keep in mind the garage sale down the street. Old toys have achieved recognition even among the flea market circuit, so the last chance to buy a marvelous pull toy at a bargain price may be in yard sales and rummages throughout urban areas. Do not count on every site to provide a wealth of available toys to plunge into your hoard, but if tempered with patience your search should be quite fruitful.

American Pre-School

Tractor Jack
73/4" long x 23/4" wide x 81/2" tall.
$30

Elephant Xylophone,
61/4" long x 41/2" wide x 8" tall.
$25

Popeye Xylophone,
9" x 101/8".
$175

Fisher-Price
ANIMALS

No. 444 Queen Buzzy Bee, 6" x 41/2".
manufactured from 1962-1985, Honey Bee Litho.
$10

No. 444 Queen Buzzy Bee, 53/4" tall x 61/2" long.
$35

Fisher-Price
ANIMALS

No. 678 Kriss Kricket,
manufactured from 1955-1958, 4" x 71/2".
$80

No. 798 Chatter
Monk, manufac-
tured from 1957-
1959, 53/4" long x
73/4" tall with tail.
$95

Fisher-Price
ANIMALS

No. 654 Tawny Tiger, manufactured from 1962-63,
© 1961, 6 1/2" long x 3 1/2" tall.
$75

No. 151 Happy Hippo, manufactured from 1962-1964, 15" x 7 1/4".
$100

Fisher-Price
ANIMALS

No. 145 Musical Elephant, with a coil spring tail
and suede-lined fabric ears, manufactured
from 1948-1951, 8" x 13".
$250

No. 735 Juggling Jumbo, manufactured
from 1958-1960, 10" long x 7 1/2" wide.
$250

Fisher-Price
ANIMALS

No. 150 Teddy Tooter,
manufactured from
1940-1942,
11" long x 141/2" tall.
$325

No. 758 Pony Chime, manufactured from 1948-1951,
61/2" wide x 131/2" long.
$250

Fisher-Price
ANIMALS

A 1968 Little Snoopy, © 1965, 41/2" x 7".
$5

No. 640 Wiggly Woofer,
manufactured from 1957-1958, 43/4" x 8".
$75

Fisher-Price
ANIMALS

No. 626 Playful Puppy with Shoe,
manufactured from 1963-1966, © 1963 – 6" long x 6" tall.
$40

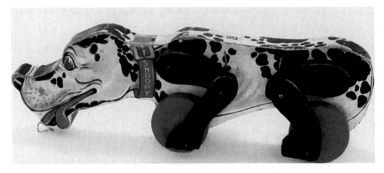

No. 180 Snoopy Sniffer, patent 1937,
manufactured from 1938-1939, 5¼" tall x 16½" long.
$45

Fisher-Price
ANIMALS

No. 462 Barky, manufactured
from 1958-1961, 41/4" x 5".
$75

No. 447 Woofy Wagger, patent 1937, manufactured from 1947-
1949, 83/4" x 91/2". The signature on litho is "F. Rojankovsky".
$75

Fisher-Price
ANIMALS

No. 445 Nosey Pup, manufactured
from 1956-1959, 63/4" x 7".
$75

No. 11 Ducky Cart, 5" tall x 8" long.
$100

Fisher-Price
ANIMALS

No. 302 Chick Basket Cart, 7" long x 7" tall.
$35

No. 795 Musical Duck, manufactured from 1952-1955,
6¼" tall x 12 1/4" long.
$75

Fisher-Price
ANIMALS

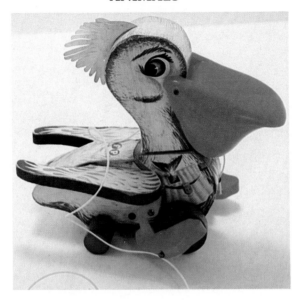

No. 794 Big Bill Pelican, patent 1961,
manufactured from 1961-1969, 8" x 8 3/4".
with fish in bill $75   without fish in bill $35

No. 141 Snap-Quack, designed by Lynn Bogue Hunt,
manufactured from 1947-1950, 7 1/4" x 11 1/2".
$175

Fisher-Price
ANIMALS

No. 767 Gabby Duck, manufactured
from 1952-1954, 6 1/2" x 8".
$100

No. 777 Gabby Goofies, patent 1947,
manufactured from 1963-1971, 5 3/4" x 13 1/2".
$15

Fisher-Price
ANIMALS

No. 695 Pinky Pig,
(this is the original version
with wooden eyes).
Manufactured from 1956-1958,
51/2" x 6" long.
$90

No. 479 Peter Pig,
manufactured from 1959-1962,
41/4" x 51/4".
$35

No. 476 Cookie Pig,
© 1965, 5" tall x 51/4" long.
$30

Fisher-Price
ANIMALS

No. 140 Katy Kackler
the Red Hen,
manufactured in 1954,
7 1/2" long x 10" tall.
$80

No. 123 Cackling Hen,
patent 1966, 6 3/4" x 10".
$15

Fisher-Price
ANIMALS

No. 656 Bossy Bell,
manufactured from
1959-1960, 53/4" x 53/4".
(This is an older design
without the bonnet).
$30

No. 155 Moo-oo Cow, manufactured from 1958-1962, 10" x 11 1/2".
$75

Fisher-Price
ANIMALS

No. 464 Gran'Pa Frog, manufactured
from 1956-1959, 5 1/4" x 5 1/4".
$75

No. 728 Buddy Bullfrog, manufactured
from 1959-1961, 6" x 6 1/4".
$100

Fisher-Price
ANIMALS

No. 496 Tiny Tim, manufactured
from 1957-1962, 3 1/2" x 6 1/4".
$35

No. 773 Tip-Toe Turtle, © 1962, manufactured
from 1962-1978, 6" x 8 1/2".
$30

Fisher-Price
ANIMALS

No. 653 Allie Gator, manufactured
from 1960-1962, 4 3/4" x 10 1/4".
$85

No. 694 Seal, © 1978,
4 3/4" x 7".
$5

Fisher-Price
ANIMALS

No. 420 Sunny Fish, © 1955, 4 3/4" tall x 6 3/4" long.
$185

No. 306 Bizzy Bunny Cart, manufactured
from 1957-1960, 7 1/4" x 9".
$50

Fisher-Price
ANIMALS

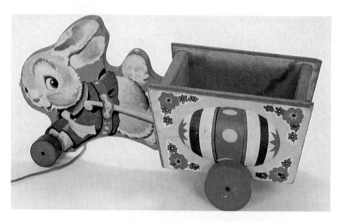

No. 401 Bunny Cart, manufactured from 1954-1957
for Easter only, 5" tall x 10" long.
$85

No. 5 Bunny Cart, manufactured from 1948-1950 for Easter only.
$100

Fisher-Price
ANIMALS

No. 525 Cottontail, 1940, Easter only.
$250

No. 131 Toy Wagon, manufactured from 1951-1955,
7 1/2" tall x 17 1/2" long.
$250

Fisher-Price
ANIMALS

No. 166 Bucky Burro, manufactured from 1955-1958,
7³/4" tall x 12" long.
$225

No. 767 Tiny Ding-Dong!, patented in 1940,
manufactured from 1940-1941, 8³/4" tall x 11" long.
$300

Fisher-Price
ANIMALS

No. 445 Hot Dog Wagon, patented in 1937,
manufactured from 1940-1942, 7" x 10 1/4", (missing bell ringer).
$150

No. 635 Tiny Teddy, © 1962, manufactured
from 1962-1967, 6 1/4" x 7 1/4".
$35

Fisher-Price
ANIMALS

No. 473 Merry Mutt,
patented in 1937,
manufactured from 1949-
1955, 71/2" x 8".
$55

No. 634 Tiny Teddy,
manufactured from
1955-1958,
61/4" long x 81/4" tall.
$75

Fisher-Price
ANIMALS

No. 480 Leo the Drummer, manufactured from 1952-1953, 7 1/2" long x 8" tall.
$225

No. 752 Teddy Zilo, patent 1937, manufactured from 1946-1948, 9" long x 10 3/4" tall.
$200

Fisher-Price
ANIMALS

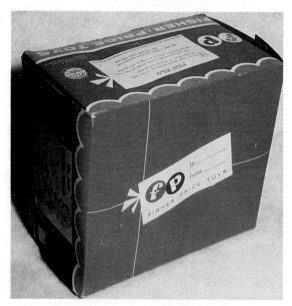

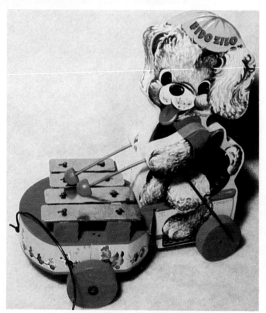

No. 707 Fido Zilo with original box,
manufactured from 1955-1958, 8" long x 10" tall.
$75   with original box - $150

Fisher-Price
ANIMALS

No. 738 Shaggy Zilo, with the original box,
manufactured from 1960-1962, 8 3/4" x 9".
$75
with original box - $150

Fisher-Price
ANIMALS

No. 737 Ziggy Zilo, manufactured from
1958-1960, 8 3/4" x 8 3/4".
$75

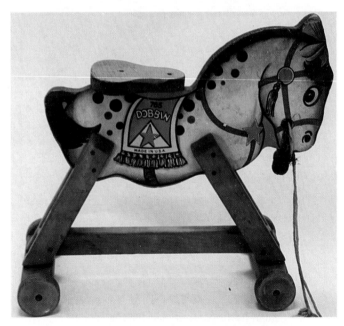

No. 765 Dandy Dobbin, manufactured
from 1941-1945, 12" long x 12" tall.
$325

Fisher-Price
WALT DISNEY

No. 177 Donald Duck Xylophone, patent 1937,
© Walt Disney Productions, British Pat. #497058,
manufactured from 1946-1953, 11" long x 13" tall.
$250

Fisher-Price
WALT DISNEY

No. 400 Donald Duck Drum
Major, patent 1939,
manufactured from 1946-1948,
7 1/2" x 9 3/4".
$200

No. 450 Donald
Duck Choo Choo,
patent 1937,
© Walt Disney
Productions, (Newer
litho version),
manufactured from
1942-1946, 7" x 8 1/2".
$75

Fisher-Price
WALT DISNEY

No. 765 Talking Donald
Duck, © Walt Disney
Productions, manufactured
from 1955-1959, 61/4" x 8".
$100

No. 510 Strutter Donald Duck, patent 1937,
manufactured in 1941, © Walt Disney Productions,
(sold thru Easter only), 10" tall x 11" long.
$200

Fisher-Price
WALT DISNEY

No. 310 Mickey Mouse Puddle Jumper, (two litho versions), manufactured from 1953-1956, © Walt Disney Productions, 5 1/2" x 6 1/2".
$75

No. 485 Mickey Mouse Choo Choo, patent 1937, manufactured from 1949-1955, © Walt Disney Productions, 7" x 8 1/2".
$100

Fisher-Price
WALT DISNEY

No. 733 Mickey Mouse Safety Patrol w/siren, manufactured from 1956-1958
© Walt Disney Productions, 7 1/8" x 9 1/2".
$200
$300 with original box

Fisher-Price
WALT DISNEY

No. 494 Pinocchio,
© 1939-Walt Disney
Productions,
manufactured from
1939-1940.
$325

No. 714 Mickey Mouse Zilo, © Walt Disney Productions,
manufactured in 1963, 8 1/4" x 9".
$175

Fisher-Price
TRANSPORTATION

No. 2017 Pilot and Plane, © 1980, 5 1/2" x 8".
$5

No. 498 Happy Little Helicopter, manufactured
from 1953-1955, 4 1/2" tall x 9" long.
$150

Fisher-Price
TRANSPORTATION

No. 448 Mini-Copter, © 1970,
43/4" x 7".
$5

No. 415 Super Jet,
manufactured
from 1952-1953,
41/4" x 91/4".
$175

No. 730 Racing
Row boat,
manufactured
from 1952-1954,
43/4" x 73/4".
$200

Fisher-Price
TRANSPORTATION

No. 139 Tuggy Tooter, patent 1967,
7 1/4" x 8 1/2".
$10

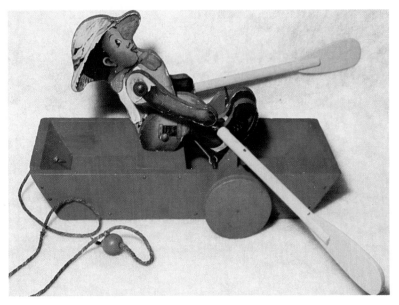

No. 155 Skipper Sam, 1934, 7" tall x 10 3/4" long.
$750

Fisher-Price
TRANSPORTATION

No. 724 Jalopy, 7" x 7 3/4".
$10

No. 724 Jalopy, (different style clown), 7" x 7".
$10

Fisher-Price
TRANSPORTATION

No. 8 Bouncy Racer, manufactured from
1960-1971, 4" x 9 1/2".
$30

No. 175 Gold Star Stagecoach, manufactured from 1954-1956,
5" wide x 8 3/4" tall x 15 3/4" long.
$250

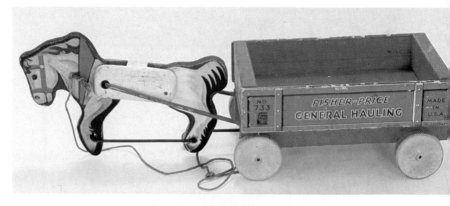

No. 733 Pony Express General Hauling,
manufactured from 1941-1945,
5 1/4" tall x 16" long.
$200

No. 161 Looky Chug-Chug, patent 1941,
manufactured from 1949-1953, 6 1/4" x 13 1/4".
$200

Fisher-Price
TRANSPORTATION

No. 616 Chuggy Pop-Up,
5 3/4" tall x 7" long.
$100

No. 643 Toot-Toot, © 1964,
4 1/8" x 6".
$10

No. 215 Fisher-Price Choo-Choo,
manufactured from 1955-1958, 3" tall x 17" long.
$100

Fisher-Price
TRANSPORTATION

No. 617 Whistling Engine,
manufactured from 1957-1958, 4 1/4" x 7 1/2".
$80

No. 999 Huffy Puffy Train, © 1963,
manufactured from 1963-1970,
4 1/2" x 26 1/4".
$35

Fisher-Price
TRANSPORTATION

No. 643 Toot-Toot, © 1964, 4 1/4" tall x 6" long.
$10

No. 629 Farmer on a Tractor, © 1961, 6" x 6".
$25

Fisher-Price
FIRE TRUCKS

No. 720 Fire Engine #1, ©1968, 3 1/2" x 7 3/4".
$5

No. 7 Looky Fire Truck,
manufactured from 1950-1954,
5" x 11 1/2".
$125

Fisher-Price
MISCELLANEOUS

No. 745 Elsie's Dairy Truck, patent 1937,
manufactured from 1948-1950, 6 3/4" x 9 1/2",
© The Bordon Co., "Driver is: Beau-Regard".
$350

No. 140 The Coaster Boy, manufactured from 1941-1942,
8 3/4" tall x 14" long.
$475

No. 757 Humpty Dumpty,
(top reads: Sat on a Wall) - (bottom reads: Had a Great Fall)
manufactured from 1957-1958, 10 1/2" wide x 10 3/4" tall.
$250

Fisher-Price
MISCELLANEOUS

No. 488, Popeye Spinach Eater, ©1929 King Features Syndicate, Inc.
Manufactured from 1939-1941, 8 1/2" x 9 3/4".
$475

Fisher-Price
MISCELLANEOUS

Pull-A-Tune Xylophone, © 1964, patent 1961,
manufactured from 1957-1970.
$25

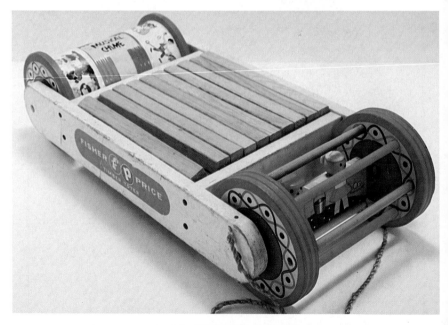

No. 910 Timber Toter,
manufactured from 1958-1959, 5 1/4" x 20 1/2".
$40

Gong Bell

Schoolboy Duckling, 8 1/2" tall x 10" long.
$35

Granny Goose, 9 1/2" x 11" x 14 1/2".
$100

Gong Bell

Baby Sandy (A Universal Pictures Star)
11" x 12 1/2".
$150

Rabbit Pull Cart with bell, 4 3/4" x 12".
$100

Gong Bell

Juggling Clown, 8 3/4" x 11 1/4".
$100

Circus Dog, 8 3/4" x 11".
$100

Gong Bell

Kewtie Kids Drummer, 9" long x 10" tall.
$150

Pudgy, 10 1/2" tall x 11 1/2" long.
$150

Gong Bell

No. 240 Boy with Puppy on Tractor,
8 3/4" tall x 9" long.
$45

Little Bo-Peep with bell, 8 1/2" x 10".
$45

Gong Bell

No. 804 Man on Tricycle,
patent May 20th, 1924, 8 1/2" tall x 9" long.
$275

Teeter-Totter Bell Toy, patent May 20th, 1920's,
8" tall x 10 1/2" long.
$135

Gong Bell

No. 302 Loco-Trix, © H.D. Allen,
7 1/2" tall x 11 1/4" long.
$100-175

Kitty Kraft, © 1939, 7 1/2" tall x 11 1/2" long.
(This pull toy still had the original price tag marked
Kruel's 5¢ to $1.00 Store, 111540 AXF 49¢).
$325

Gong Bell

Noah's Ark,
5 1/2" tall x 13 3/4" long.
$55

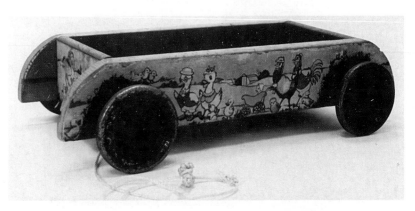

Pull Wagon decorated with ducks and chickens,
4" tall x 15" long.
$40

Holgate Toys

Cart with Shape Blocks, 3 1/2" tall x 5" wide x 11" long.
$35

Dump Cart with Building Blocks, 6 1/4" tall x 11" long.
$80

Holgate Toys

Wood Cart, 2 1/4" tall x 11 1/8" long.
$5

Big H Wagon, 2 3/4" tall x 15 3/4" long (without blocks)
3 1/2" tall x 15 3/4" long (with blocks in the wagon).
$150

Holgate Toys

Block Holder Cart, 2 1/4" x 8 1/4",
(the blocks are missing).
$20

Tip-Over Duck, patent 1944,
5 1/4" wide x 5 1/2" tall x 8 1/2" long.
$95

Holgate Toys

Jack Rabbit Bus, No. HT640/PSC12,
the top is removable, 4" tall x 12 1/4" long.
(original Lazarus tag of $3.00).
$75

Hook and Ladder, 3 1/2" x 13 5/8".
$75

Holgate Toys

Wood Canoe, 3" x 10", (pieces are missing).
$35

Ship with Sailors,
the ship is 2 3/4" tall x 11" long,
the sailors are 3 7/8" tall.
$75

Holgate Toys

Wood Tractor, 4" tall x 6 1/4" long.
$85

No. H.T. 670 U.S. Army Ambulance, 4 1/4" tall x 9" long.
$95

Holgate Toys

No. 669 U.S. Army Tank, 4 1/4" tall x 11" long.
$125

Race Car with peg people, 2 3/4" tall x 11" long.
(People are 3 1/2" tall).
$45

Holgate Toys

Car with People,
the car is 2 1/4" tall x 7 1/4" long,
the people are 2 1/8" tall & some are 1 1/2" tall.
$95

Station Wagon with People,
2 7/8" tall x 8 1/2" long.
$95

Holgate Toys

Car with top and people inside,
3 1/2" tall x 8 1/4" long.
$95

Army Transport "U.S.", 2 1/2" x 9".
$95

Holgate Toys

Car with Camper, 3 1/2" x 15 1/2".
$65

Train Set (5 cars), overall length 34 1/2".
(See individual cars for specific size).
$75

Holgate Toys

Train Set Engine, 4 3/8" tall x 8 1/2" long.
$75 for the set

Rail Car part of the train set, marked
"3 Wise Men of Gotham", 3" tall x 6" long.
$75 for the set

Holgate Toys

Rail Car marked "Blynken - Nod",
3" tall x 7 1/4" long.
$75 for the set

Rail Car marked "3 Men in a Tub",
3" tall x 6 1/2" long.
$75 for the set

Holgate Toys

Rail Car marked "Cinderella's Coach",
4 5/8" tall x 6 1/4" long.
$75 for the set

No. 207 Train with center car and caboose,
marked Cass Limited on side, possibly Holgate.
Engine - 3 1/2" tall x 12" long
Center Car - 2 3/4" tall x 8" long
Caboose - 3 1/2" tall x 8" long
$50

Hustler Toys

Larry Hustler and his horse,
8" long x 8 1/2" tall.
$100

Poncho Hustler
$200

Hustler Toys

Hiram Hustler
$125

Sambo Hustler
$250

Hustler Toys

Horse and Jockey, 7 1/4".
$125

Hustler Twins with original box.
$250

Hustler Toys

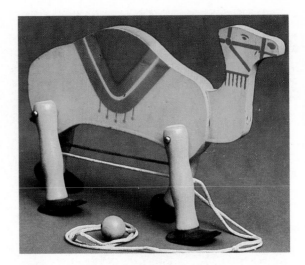

Camel
$100

Betty Roll Duck,
made prior to 1925.
$75

Hustler Toys

Watch Dog
$200

Billy Hustler
$200

Hustler Toys

Boy in Push-Pull Cart, advertising for "Happy Ham Farm
Products, Newton & Thompson Mfg. Co., Brandon, VT,
6" tall x 10" long. (Possibly Hustler)
$150

Doc Hustler, 6 1/8" tall x 13 3/4" long.
$175

Hustler Toys

Push & Pull Car, 5 1/2" tall x 11" long.
$175

Pete Hustler Transfer, 5 1/2" tall x 10 1/2" long.
$200

Joe Hustler Transfer, 5 1/2" x 10 1/4".
$175

N. N. Hill Brass Co.

Monkey on a Tricycle,
6 1/4" tall x 6 1/2" long.
$60

Monki-Wheeler, 7 1/2" x 9".
$85

N. N. Hill Brass Co.

Delivery Duck, 7 3/4" tall x 9 1/2" long.
$65

Duckling Cart, 6 1/2" tall x 11 1/4" long.
$65

Duckling Two Wheeler, 7 3/4" x 8 3/4".
$65

Rabbit Cart, 12 1/2" tall x 17" long.
$65

N. N. Hill Brass Co.

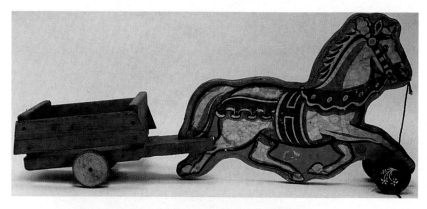

Horse with Cart, 4 3/4" wide x 8 1/2" tall x 20" long.
$50

Horse and Pull Cart with bell, 5 3/4" x 12 3/4".
$75

Black Horse and Cart, 5" tall x 12 1/4" long.
$20

N. N. Hill Brass Co.

Young Cowboy on a Pony, 8" long x 8 3/4" tall.
$125

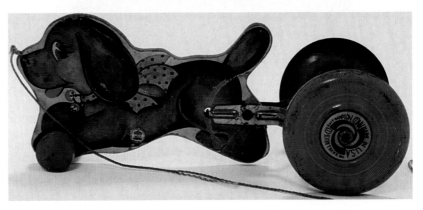

Brown Puppy with Bow and Cart,
4 1/2" tall x 10 1/2" long.
$65

N. N. Hill Brass Co.

Yoo-Hoo It's Me Pinky Lee,
© 1955 National Broadcasting Co., Inc.,
7 1/4" long x 10 1/4" tall.
$175

Rich Toys

Rich's Little Milk Man,
10 1/2" tall x 20" long.
$400

No. 257 Horse Drawn Milk Wagon with Rider,
Advertising Borden's Golden Crest Grade A Milk,
11 1/2" tall x 18" long.
$475

Rich Toys

Horse with Cart, 7 1/2" tall x 15 1/2" long.
$250

Girl jumping rope, (actual title unknown).
$250

Toy Tinkers

The Tinker Mule, ca. 1929.
$225

Whirly Tinker, 7" wide x 7" tall x 8 1/4" long.
$95

Toy Tinkers

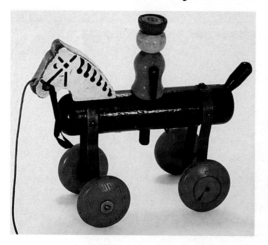

Pony Tinker,
6 1/2" tall x 7 1/2" long.
$200

Racing Dogs,
4 1/4" x 7 1/2".
$70

Choo-Choo Tinker Railway, 3 3/4" x 13 1/2".
$50

Miscellaneous Manufacturers

No. 439 Cowboy Joe's Musical Chuck Wagon,
manufactured by Mattel Inc., Los Angeles, patent 1950,
© 1951, 6 1/2" tall x 12" long.
$75

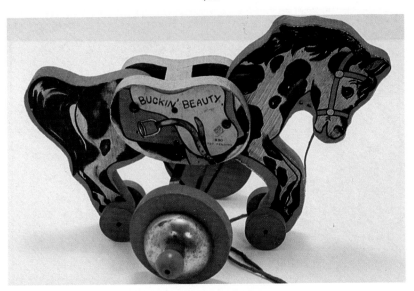

No. 930 Buckin' Beauty, manufactured
by Brice Toy Novelty Inc., Colden, NY, 6 1/2" x 11".
$75

Miscellaneous Manufacturers

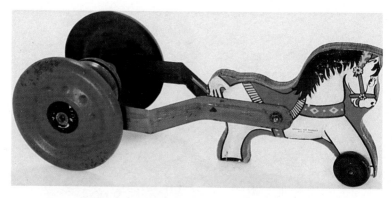

Pony with Bell Cart, manufactured by General Toy Product,
made in Canada, 5 1/4" tall x 13 1/2" long.
$50

Ted-Toy Express, manufactured
by International Toy Corp., A Ted Toy.
$90

Miscellaneous Manufacturers

Fran-Zell "The Walking-Barking Dog" with original box,
manufactured by Frantz Toys, later known as Hustler Toy Corp.,
the dog is 4" wide x 7 1/4" long x 7 3/4" tall.
$250 with box

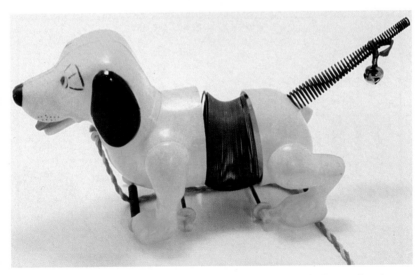

Slinky Dog, manufactured by James Industries Inc., Paoli, Pennsylvania,
1950's, 6 1/8" x 12 1/2" (when body is together as pictured).
$15
(also available in many different characters such as a: seal, worm, soldiers, hand car, train, and Bucko.)

Miscellaneous Manufacturers

Elsie the Cow that jumped over the Moon,
© Borden Co., by Wood Commodities Corp., NY, NY,
5 3/4" wide x 9" long x 10 1/4" tall.
$200

No. 410 Zoo-Apart, manufactured
by StromBecker, made in the USA.
$70

Miscellaneous Manufacturers

Ducky Waddles, manufactured by Wyandotte Toys,
6 3/4" tall x 8" long.
$75

Steiff Goose
$175

Miscellaneous Manufacturers

Elephant, manufactured by Tick-Tock Toys,
designed exclusively for Firestone, 8" tall x 14" long.
$75

Donkey Mechanical Pull Toy,
manufactured by Modern Toys of Japan, 6" tall x 9" long.
$40

Miscellaneous Manufacturers

Marching Soldier,
A Ted Toy,
manufactured by
The Ted Toy-Lers Inc.,
New Bedford, Mass.,
6 1/2" long x 9 3/4" tall.
$175

Felix-The-Cat
Delivery Cart,
8 3/4" tall x 10" long.
$550

Miscellaneous Manufacturers

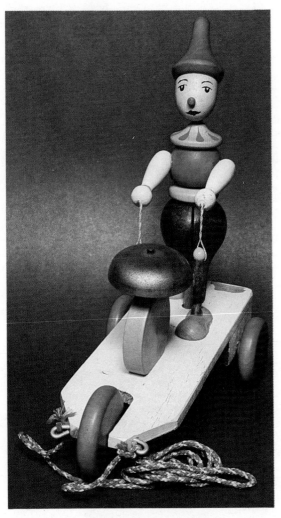

Clown with bell pull toy,
manufactured by Kohner.
$100

Miscellaneous Manufacturers

Marching Majorette Drummer,
manufactured by Keystone, 10 1/4" tall x 10 3/4" long.
$125

Slinky Soldiers with original box, catalog no. 375,
manufactured by James Industries Inc., of Paoli, PA.
$75 with box

Miscellaneous Manufacturers

Cantaloupe Dump Truck,
5 1/2" tall x 8 1/2" long.
$10

Teddy Giant Galloping Jockey,
manufactured by The Ted Toy-Lers Inc.
$275

Miscellaneous Manufacturers

Tiny Tot Peg and Ball Cart with original box,
manufactured by Jaymar Specialty Co., NY, 4" tall x 6 1/2" long.
$45 with box

Playskool Wagon with blocks, manufactured by Playskool,
3 1/2" tall x 12 3/4" long.
$35

Miscellaneous Manufacturers

Spinning Letter Blocks, manufactured by
Kingsbury Toys, Keene, NH, 4" tall x 5" wide x 8" long.
$30

No. SS7 Dump Truck, manufactured by Michigan's Toy,
6 1/2" tall x 15 1/4" long.
$30

Miscellaneous Manufacturers

Train, manufactured by Childhood Interests Inc.,
5 1/2" tall x 14 1/2" long.
$15

Little Jasper, with original box,
manufactured by Wood Commodities Corp., NY,
© George Pal Puppetoons, released by Paramount Pictures Inc.,
7 1/2" long x 9 1/2" tall.
$250 with original box

Unknown Manufacturers

Cricket/Grasshopper,
3 1/2" wide x 5 3/4" tall x 12" long.
$35

Grasshopper, all plastic,
6 1/2" tall x 11" long.
$30

Unknown Manufacturers

Turtle, made in Japan,
1 3/4" tall x 4 1/2" long.
$15

No. 2 Race Car with Man,
4 1/4" tall x 7 1/4" long.
$15

Unknown Manufacturers

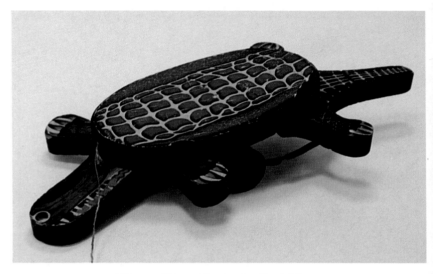

Alligator/Crocodile, 2 3/4" tall x 16" long.
$35

Two Horses with a Wagon,
"patent pending" stamped on bottom, 6 1/2" tall x 18 1/2" long.
$200

Unknown Manufacturers

1936 Mallard Duck, patent no. 2054567,
(marked others pending on the wing),
3 1/2" wide x 8 1/2" tall x 9" long.
$45

Country Style Duck, 6" tall x 8 1/4" long.
$65

Unknown Manufacturers

Duck Egg Cart, (1930-1940), 3 1/4" x 7 1/4".
$35

Duck Cart, 8 1/2" tall x 12" long.
$40

Unknown Manufacturers

Mr. Monk,
wood and paper litho, 3 1/4" long x 5" tall.
$25

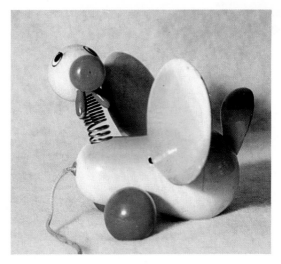

Duck Pull Toy with spring neck,
5" tall x 5 3/4" long.
$15

Unknown Manufacturers

English Setter/Cocker Spaniel (could be either)
7 1/2" tall x 10 1/2" long.
$60

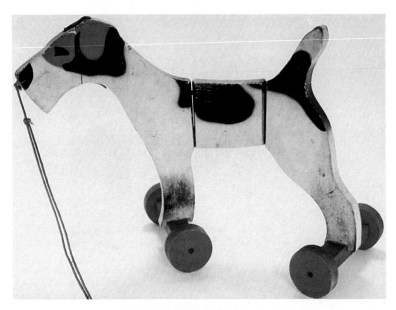

Scottish Terrier, 13" tall x 19" long.
$75

Unknown Manufacturers

Humpty Dumpty sat on a wall,
5 1/4" x 6 1/2".
$100

Witch Trick-or-Treater with
a Jack-O-Lantern, 4 1/2" tall.
$75

Unknown Manufacturers

Man in a Truck, tin litho,
3 1/4" tall x 7 1/2" long.
$125

Man on a Tractor, 4 1/2" wide x 5 3/4" tall x 8" long.
$35

Unknown Manufacturers

Man driving a Truck, tin,
3 1/2" tall x 7 1/4" long.
$100

Helicopter, marked Woodette Helicopter,
4 3/4" tall x 12" long.
$65

Unknown Manufacturers

Helicopter, (note: missing blades and back wheel)
4 3/4" tall x 10 3/4" long.
$60 complete

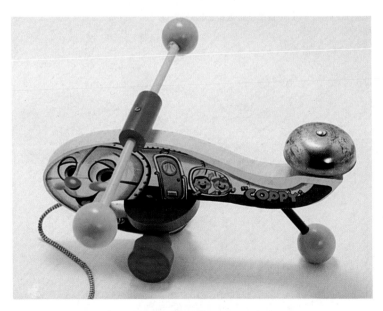

"Coppy" The Happy Helicopter with bell,
5" tall x 9" long.
$30

Unknown Manufacturers

Girl with moving legs, 4 3/4" long x 5 1/4" tall.
$20

Boy on a Tricycle.
$40

Unknown Manufacturers

Speedy Felix, wooden, 14" tall x 14" long.
$450

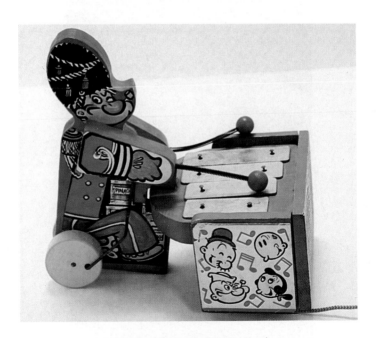

Popeye Majorette Xylophone,
8 1/4" x 8 3/4".
$200

Unknown Manufacturers

SS Popeye Boat, litho,
3" wide x 4" tall x 10" long.
$225

Casper The Friendly Ghost and his friends,
9 1/4" long x 10" tall.
$200

Unknown Manufacturers

Water Wheel,
7" tall x 10 1/4" long.
$15

Double Twirler,
stamped in the metal "Made in USA",
4 1/4" wide x 6" tall x 11" long.
$50